VERY EASY RECORDER TUNES

Anthony Marks

Edited by Jenny Tyler
Designed by Doriana Berkovic

Illustrated by Simone Abel
and Kim Blundell

Music selected, arranged and edited by Anthony Marks
New compositions by Anthony Marks
Recorder advisor: Ruth Ellis
Music setting: Andrew Jones
Managing designer: Russell Punter

SCHOLASTIC INC.

New York Toronto London Auckland Sydney
Mexico City New Delhi Hong Kong Buenos Aires

About this book

You will already know some of these tunes, though others might be less familiar. Some of them were written specially for this book. If you have a computer, you can listen to all the tunes on the Usborne Quicklinks Website to hear how they go. Just go to **www.usborne-quicklinks.com** and enter the keywords "very easy recorder tunes", then follow the simple instructions.

At the start of every piece there is a picture in a circle. Each picture has a sticker to match it in the middle of the book. Use the stickers to show when you have learned a piece.

Contents

Recorder reminders

On this page you will find some hints and tips to help you enjoy your recorder playing more. You can read these first, or go straight to the music on page 4 and come back here if you want some reminders.

If you need to know the fingering for a particular note, there is a chart on page 32 showing how to play all the most common notes on the recorder.

Where to put your fingers

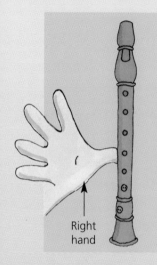

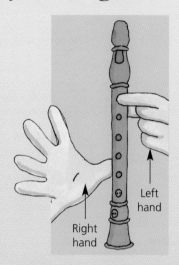

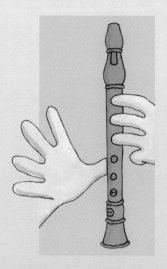

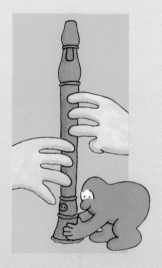

Place your right thumb on the back of the recorder between the fourth and fifth holes to hold it steady.

Then cover the hole on the back with your left thumb. Cover the top hole on the front with your first finger.

Then cover the next two holes with the second and third finger of your left hand.

Then cover the other holes with your right-hand fingers. Your little finger covers the holes at the bottom.

Making a good sound

Here are a few hints to help you make a good sound when you play.

Sit or stand up straight when you play . . .

. . . but try to stay relaxed and comfortable.

Make sure your fingers cover the holes properly.

Say "t" or "tuh" very gently as you blow each note. This makes the sound crisp and clear.

Don't blow too hard, or you will make a squeaky sound.

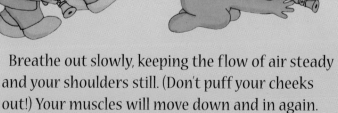

Breathing

When you play, you need to breathe in a special way. At first, practice this without your recorder. Breathe in slowly through your mouth. Keep your shoulders still but not stiff. If you place a hand lightly on your stomach, just below your ribs, you will feel your muscles move outwards and upwards as you breathe in.

Breathe out slowly, keeping the flow of air steady and your shoulders still. (Don't puff your cheeks out!) Your muscles will move down and in again.
Try this lying on the floor with a small book on the area just below your ribs. As you breathe in and out slowly, the book will move up and down.
Remember these muscles every time you play, and use them to help you breathe evenly.

3

Go and tell Aunt Nancy

This is an old American folk tune. Before you begin, play the notes B, A and G a few times to get used to them.

Au clair de la lune

This French tune was written in the 17th century. On page 15 you can find a longer version of it, and more about who wrote it.

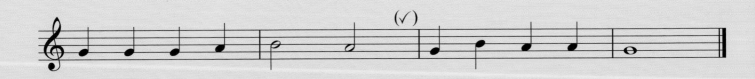

Merrily we roll along

This is an old American song. The tune is like the nursery rhyme "Mary had a little lamb". Nobody knows which came first.

4

La capucine

"La capucine" is a French nursery rhyme from the 18th century. "Capucine" is French for "nasturtium", a kind of flower.

Fais dodo

This is an old French lullaby. "Dodo" is a childish word for "sleep", so "Fais dodo" means "Go to sleep". Try to play the music gently and evenly.

Breath marks

In the music you will see little marks like this: ✓ . These show you good places to take a breath. Sometimes you will see these marks in brackets. These tell you to take a breath if you need to, but you don't have to.

Try to take a breath only where you see a mark. The music may sound odd if you breathe in other places. If you need to breathe more often, ask your teacher to show you where.

5

Underneath the apple tree

This tune was written specially for this book. Count the bars of three beats very carefully. Take breaths in the rests, but make sure you keep counting.

Highland laddie

This tune is for one or two players. Play the top line of music, and ask your teacher or a friend to play the lower one. There is more about playing tunes with other people on page 11.

Try playing the lower part yourself, too.

O'Connor's reel

This is an old Irish folk tune. It might help to learn the first two lines first. Then, when you can play those, learn the rest.

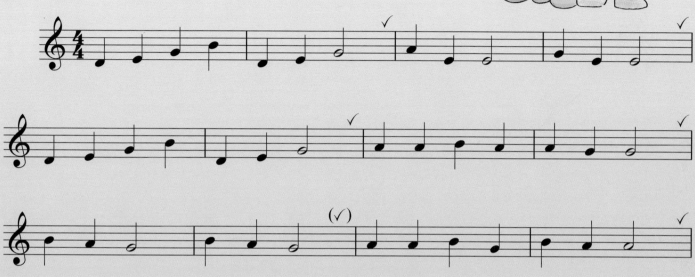

Give me your hand

"Give me your hand" is an old English folk tune. Make sure you hold the last note for a full three beats.

Aiken Drum

"Aiken Drum" is an old Scottish marching tune. It was first published in 1841 and became popular as a nursery rhyme.

Pease pudding hot

Pease pudding is made from dried peas and bacon. It was popular in medieval times, when this song was first sung. Watch out for the short notes!

The grand old Duke of York

This tune was written in the 18th century. The Duke of York was the son of King George III of England. He fought wars in France and Holland.

Happy as a lark

Can you think of ways to make this tune sound happy? Try playing it fast, then slow. Which works best?

À la claire fontaine

This is a Canadian tune. Its title is French for "By the clear fountain". French people first went to live in Canada in the 17th century.

Sur le pont d'Avignon

This is a French tune. The title means "On the bridge at Avignon", though people used to dance on an island in the river under the bridge, not on top of it.

10

Hot cross buns!

Hot cross buns are sweet bread rolls with a cross sign on the top. When market traders sold them, they sang this tune to attract customers.

This tune is for two players. Find out more below.

Tunes for two players

A tune for two players is called a duet. In a duet, one person plays the top line of music while someone else plays the lower one.

Before you try this, play your own part until you know it well. (It can help to learn the other part too, so that you know what the other person is going to play.)

Then, when you play with someone else, count a few bars together before you start so that you begin at the same time.

When you both know the music, try exchanging parts.

You could also record one part and play the other over the top.

Bobby Shafto

"Bobby Shafto" was first sung in the
north of England in the 18th century.
It is about a sailor who goes away to sea.

Down by the watermill

This tune uses one four-bar rhythm,
repeated four times. Only the notes change.
You could make up a tune of your own by
repeating a rhythm using different notes.

Write your rhythm
down first, then
choose your notes.

Streets of Laredo

Laredo is a city in Texas, near the border between America and Mexico. This is an old cowboy tune. The bottom line is a duet part for another player.

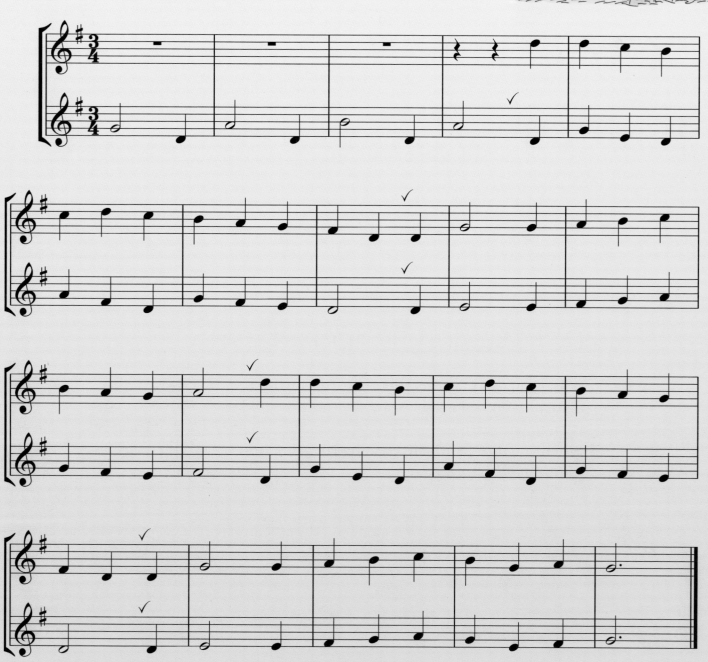

If you play this as a duet, the person playing the top line waits nearly four bars before starting, while the lower line plays an introduction.

If you like, you can both play the introduction. You could also make up a duet part to go with it. Use the same rhythm, but experiment until you find notes that fit with the written part.

Hint: the note D fits with all the notes in the introduction.

13

Twinkle, twinkle, little star

This nursery rhyme is so old that nobody knows who wrote it or when. There are versions of it in many different languages.

Old Macdonald had a farm

When you can play this tune, try starting it on G instead. (You will need low D.) Then try "Twinkle, twinkle" starting on low D. (You will need F sharp.) When you do this, it helps to sing the tune first, to remind you how it sounds.

Au clair de la lune

Some people say this tune is by Jean-Baptiste Lully, a composer who worked at the court of the French king, Louis XVI. The title means "In the moonlight".

There's a hole in my bucket

This is an American tune. Count carefully, because you have to begin on the third beat of the bar. Don't rush the short notes.

Steps and jumps

Sometimes tunes move by steps from one note to the next. Sometimes they move by jumps. Look for the steps and jumps in the tunes on these pages.

15

Long, long ago

Thomas Haynes Bayley, an English poet, wrote this song in 1833. In 1843 it was published in America, where it was very popular for many years.

O, du lieber Augustin

This is a very old German folk tune. Its title means "My dear Augustin". In English the tune is sometimes known as "Buy a broom".

Michael Finnegan

Make sure you play the short notes in a precise, clear rhythm. Keep your fingers close to the recorder so that they don't have far to move.

This old man

This is a very old nursery rhyme, sometimes known as "Nick nack paddywack". Make sure you play the rhythms very precisely.

Frère Jacques

The title of this old French song means "Brother James". It is about a monk who sleeps too late in the morning.

Row, row, row your boat

Try to play this smoothly and gently. Imagine you are rowing in a boat on a calm day. Don't rush the third beat of the bar.

Rounds

A round is a tune that can be played by several people. All the tunes on these two pages are rounds. Each person starts a few bars apart, as shown by the numbers in boxes on the music.
  When the first player gets to number 2, the second player starts at the beginning. When the first player gets to number 3, the third player starts, and so on. You have to decide how many times you are each going to play the tune, then stop one by one.

The tunes on this page can be played by up to four people, but they will work with two or three as well. If there is just you, they will work as solos too. If there are lots of players, more than one person can play each part.

18

Old Abram Brown

This is an English folk song about an old man who has died. Can you make it sound sad? Does it sound best fast or slow?

London's burning

People sang this tune after the Great Fire of London in 1666. The fire burned for five days and thousands of buildings were destroyed.

Clue: play backwards from the end!

Jacques comes back!

This is a new tune that uses the same notes as "Frère Jacques", but not in the same order. Can you work out what has happened? You can still play it as a round.

Jingle bells

James Pierpont, an American musician in Savannah, Georgia, wrote the words and music for this tune. It was published in 1857.

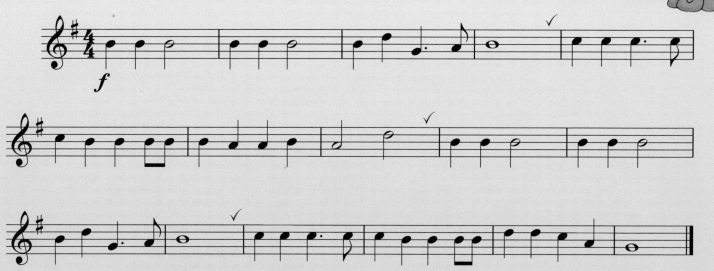

Auld lang syne

This Scottish song was first written down in the 18th century by the poet Robert Burns. People sing it on New Year's Eve. The title means "Old times".

Hark, the herald angels sing

This tune was written in the 19th century by a German composer, Felix Mendelssohn. It is based on words by Charles Wesley, an English preacher.

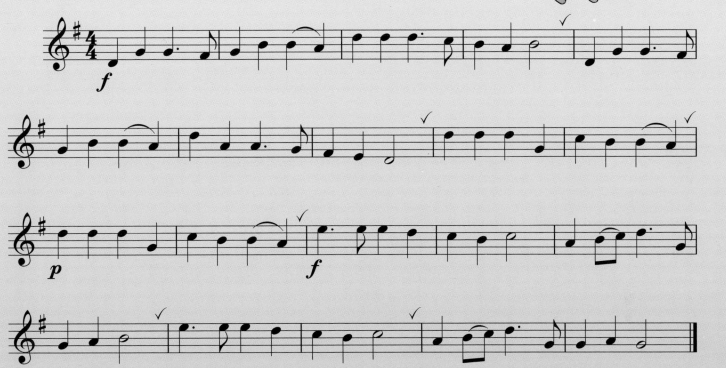

Away in a manger

An American composer, William James Kilpatrick, wrote this tune in Philadelphia in the 19th century. Play it quietly, like a lullaby.

Lullaby

This tune was written by Franz Schubert, an Austrian composer who lived in the 19th century. Play it slowly and quietly, without rushing. Make the slurred notes run smoothly together.

Wedding march

A German composer, Richard Wagner, wrote this tune in the 19th century. It is from the opera (a play with music) "Lohengrin", and is played during a wedding scene.

22

Spring (from "The Four Seasons")

"The Four Seasons" is a set of pieces by Vivaldi, an Italian composer who lived from 1678 to 1741. The trill in the last bar tells you to alternate quickly between A and B for as long as the note lasts.

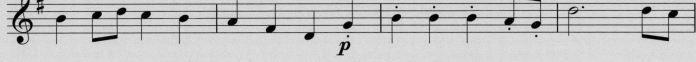

Playing loudly and quietly

In this piece, you have to play some parts loudly and others more quietly. Because it can be hard to do this on the recorder, it helps to learn a few tricks. To make a loud sound, blow slightly harder and hold each note for its full length. To make a quiet sound, blow more softly and make the notes a little shorter than normal.

This sign tells you to play loudly.

This sign tells you to play quietly.

The cuckoo

You can play this old French nursery rhyme as a round (see page 18). There are two types of cuckoo call in this tune – can you spot them both?

Land of the silver birch

This is a Canadian tune. Play it lightly and make sure you don't rush the short notes! Does it sound better fast or slow? Try it both ways, then decide.

Lavender's blue

This is a 17th-century English song. Lavender is a sweet-smelling plant. People believed it would help them sleep and give them pleasant dreams.

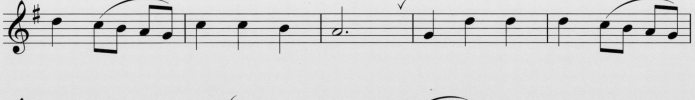

Benjamin Bowlabags

This tune was written in the 19th century when England was at war with France. It is from Cornwall, in southwest England. It is also known as "The Proud Tailor".

Taking quick breaths

In "Benjamin Bowlabags" there are not many places to take a breath, so you have to breathe in quickly. Try making the note before the breath a little shorter to give yourself time.

Take in plenty of air to last until the next breath. (Don't rush - if you do, you won't take enough air in.)

Men of Harlech

"Men of Harlech" is an old Welsh song. It is about a battle that took place in the 15th century, but the song was probably written many years later.

Playing in different styles

Once you know the notes to a piece of music, you need to think about other things. Should it be loud or quiet? Fast or slow? Smooth or spiky? Think about this when you play "Men of Harlech".
 In this book there are some signs in the music to help you decide. Use these as a guide, but remember that they are only suggestions. Try other versions and compare them to see which you like best. This is part of your skill as a player.

Ho la hi

This is a German folk tune. Watch out for the C sharps. (If you need help finding this note, look at page 32.)

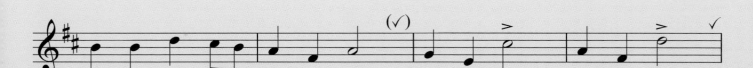

Helston floral dance

Helston is a village in Cornwall in the southwest of England. Every year in May there is a special ceremony and people dance to this music.

The Lord's my shepherd

This hymn tune was written by Jessie Irvine, who lived from 1836 to 1887. It is also known as "Crimond", which is the town in Scotland where Irvine lived.

Now is the month of Maying

An English composer, Thomas Morley, wrote this tune around 1595. He was the organist at Saint Paul's Cathedral in London. Look out for the repeat signs in this tune: you have to play each section twice.

Hymn to joy

A German composer, Ludwig van Beethoven, wrote this tune in 1827. It is now the anthem of the European Union.

Scarborough fair

This English tune was first sung in the Middle Ages. Once a year there was a huge market and fair in the seaside town of Scarborough.

Watch out for the tied notes!

In an English country garden

This is an old dance tune. When you know it well, try it a different way. In each group of two short notes, make the first a little longer than the second.

What shall we do with the drunken sailor?

This is a sea shanty. Sailors sang shanties while they pulled ropes, keeping time with the music. This made the work easier. As in the tune above, try playing the pairs of short notes unevenly. Which version do you prefer?

O come, all ye faithful

Both the Christmas carols on this page were first sung in the 18th century, but nobody knows who wrote them.

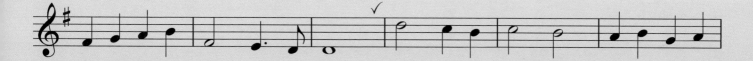

The first Nowell

The sign "cresc." is short for "crescendo", the Italian for "get louder". It will sound most effective if you get louder bit by bit until you reach the middle of the last line.

31

Notes on the recorder

This chart shows fingerings for the most common notes on the recorder. When you see a black circle, cover the hole with your finger. An empty circle means you leave the hole uncovered. Sometimes the thumb circle is half-filled.

This means you half cover the hole. This helps you play higher notes.

Some notes have different names but the same fingering: D sharp/E flat; A sharp/B flat.

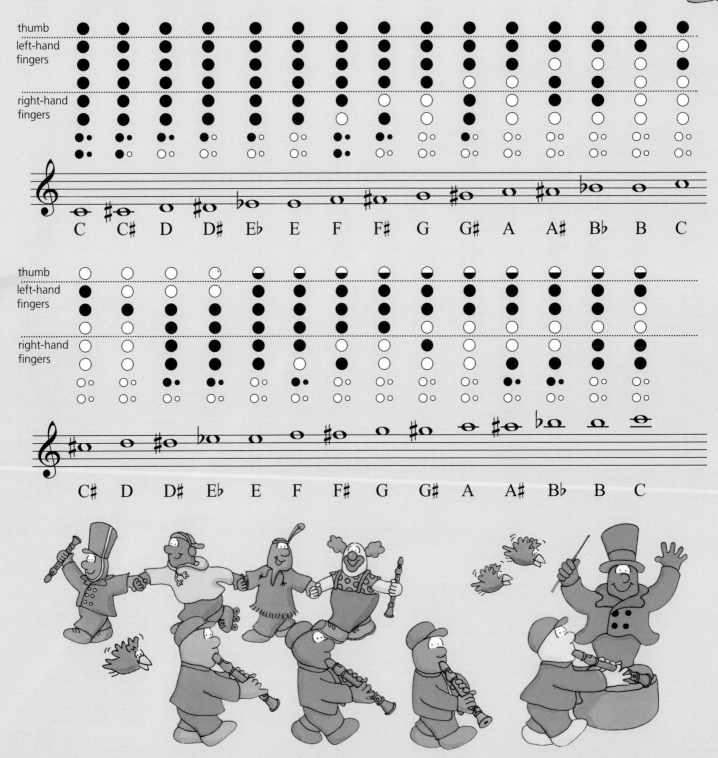

ISBN 0-439-68688-1

12 11 10 9 8 7 6 5 4 3 2 1   4 5 6 7 8 9/0

Printed in the U.S.A.   08

First Scholastic printing, November 2004